TRINITY
GUILDHALL

CW00422376

Piano
Grade 8

Pieces & Exercises
for Trinity Guildhall examinations

2012-2014

Published by
Trinity College London
Registered Office:
89 Albert Embankment
London SE1 7TP UK

T +44 (0)20 7820 6100
F +44 (0)20 7820 6161
E music@trinityguildhall.co.uk
www.trinityguildhall.co.uk

Registered in the UK
Company no. 02683033
Charity no. 1014792

Copyright © 2011 Trinity College London

Unauthorised photocopying is illegal
No part of this publication may be copied or reproduced in any
form or by any means without the prior permission of the publisher.

Printed in England by Halstan & Co. Ltd, Amersham, Bucks.

Air and Variations in E

The Harmonious Blacksmith HWV 430

George Frideric Handel
(1685–1759)

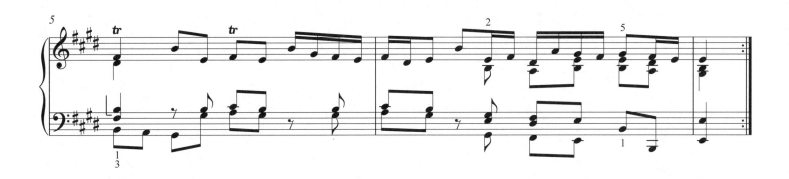

The repeats marked with an asterisk (*) should be played in the examination for balance.

Copyright © 2011 Trinity College London

Variation 2

Variation 5

Più tosto allegro con espressione

1st movt from Sonata in F# minor, op. 25 no. 5

Muzio Clementi
(1752–1832)

Più tosto allegro con espressione [♩ = 69–80]

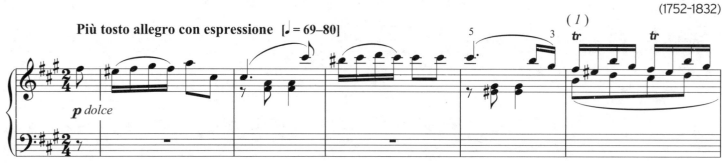

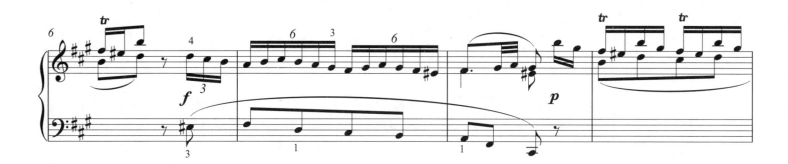

(*1*) Played as a mordent.

Copyright © 2011 Trinity College London

(2) Starting on the upper note.

Romance in F#

op. 28 no. 2

Robert Schumann
(1810-1856)

Copyright © 2011 Trinity College London

(*1*) Left hand takes over right hand A.

Intermezzo

op. 119 no. 3

Johannes Brahms
(1833-1897)

Copyright © 2011 Trinity College London

You may photocopy this page to avoid a page turn.

Scottish Legend

no. 1 from *Two Pieces* op. 54

Amy Beach
(1867–1944)

Fingerings have been suggested for examination purposes only.

Copyright © 2002 Alfred Music Publishing Co., Inc.
All Rights Reserved. Used by Permission.

Bird's Tale

from *Romantic Sketches for the Young* op. 54

Nicolai Medtner
(1880–1951)

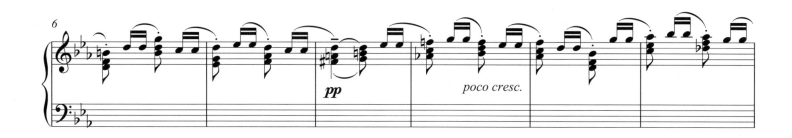

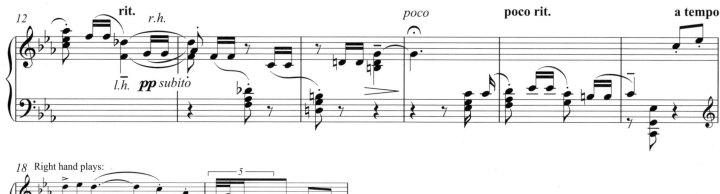

Some fingerings have been suggested for examination purposes only.

 Copyright © 1932 by Musikverlag Zimmermann, Frankfurt/Main (Germany). Used with written consent of the Publisher.

Copyright © 1932 by Musikverlag Zimmermann, Frankfurt/Main (Germany). Used with written consent of the Publisher.

22   Copyright © 1932 by Musikverlag Zimmermann, Frankfurt/Main (Germany). Used with written consent of the Publisher.

Copyright © 1932 by Musikverlag Zimmermann, Frankfurt/Main (Germany). Used with written consent of the Publisher.

La colombe (The Dove)

no. 1 from *Préludes*

Olivier Messiaen
(1908-1992)

Lent, expressif, d'une sonorité très enveloppée [♪ = 56–63]

Copyright © 1930 Editions Durand

Blue Air

from *Colour Suite*

Madeleine Dring
(1923-1977)

Fingerings have been suggested for examination purposes only.

  Copyright © 1963 Josef Weinberger Limited. Reproduced by permission of the copyright owners.

[Blank page to facilitate page turns]

Barcarolle

no. 1

Ned Rorem
(born 1923)

Composer's metronome mark ♩. = **66**.
Fingerings have been suggested for examination purposes only.

Copyright © 1963 by Henmar Press, Inc., New York.
Reprinted by permission of Peters Edition Limited, London.
International copyright secured. All rights reserved.

Exercises

1a. Which way is up? I don't know! – tone, balance and voicing

1b. Song of Love – tone, balance and voicing

Dynamics have been left to the candidate's discretion.

Copyright © 2011 Trinity College London

2a. Deliberato – co-ordination

2b. Follow My Leader – co-ordination

Copyright © 2011 Trinity College London

3a. Strides – finger & wrist strength and flexibility

3b. Uncompromising – finger & wrist strength and flexibility

Copyright © 2011 Trinity College London